AGES 4-5
Reception

Gold Stars®

Maths

Parragon

Bath · New York · Cologne · Melbourne · Delhi
Hong Kong · Shenzhen · Singapore · Amsterdam

Helping your child

⭐ Remember that the activities in this book should be enjoyed by your child. Try to find a quiet place to work.

⭐ Your child does not need to complete each page in one go. Always stop before your child grows tired, and come back to the same page another time.

⭐ It is important to work through the pages in the right order because the activities get progressively more difficult.

⭐ The answers to the activities are on page 32.

⭐ Always give your child lots of encouragement and praise.

⭐ Remember that the gold stars are a reward for effort as well as for achievement.

Written by Frances Mackay
Educational consultant: Dr Janet Rose
Illustrated by Simon Abbot and Adam Linley

First published by Parragon Books Ltd in 2015
Parragon Books Ltd
Chartist House
15-17 Trim Street
Bath BA1 1HA, UK

ISBN: 978-1-4723-9236-7

Printed in China

Contents

Counting to 5

Count the bees. Point to the number.
Trace it with your finger. Write the numbers.

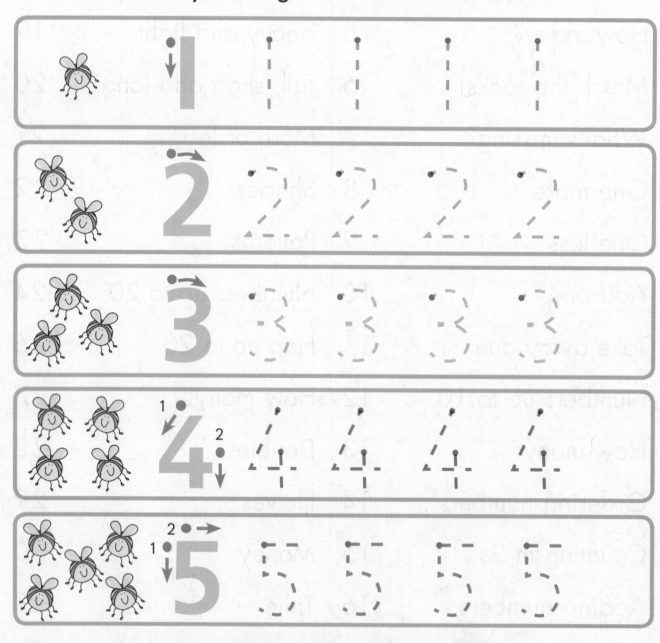

1 2 3 4 5

How many?

Count the bugs. Write the answers in the boxes.

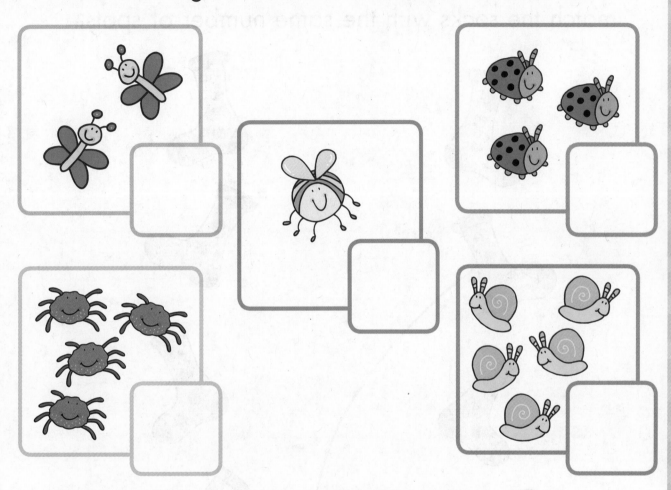

Draw five spots on the ladybird. Colour it in.

Match the socks

Count the spots on each sock. Draw lines to match the socks with the same number of spots.

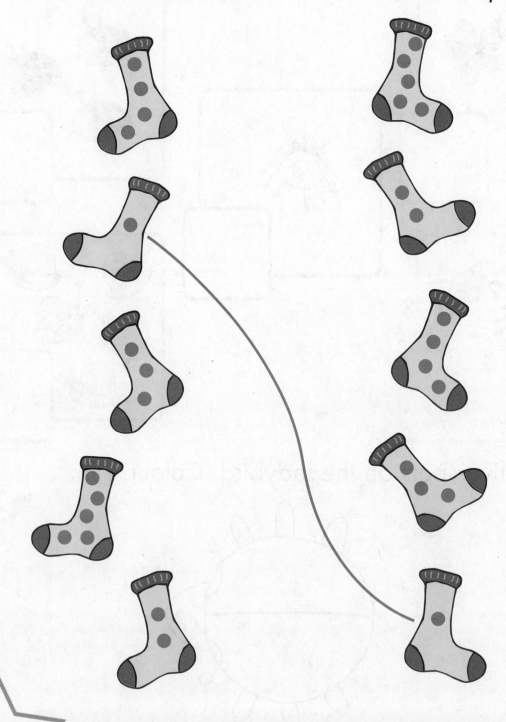

What's missing?

Write the missing numbers.

Draw the missing things.

Note for parent: Working out the missing objects prepares your child for adding and subtracting.

7

One more

Draw 1 more. Count the objects. How many are there altogether? Write the numbers in the boxes.

draw 1 more — 3

draw 1 more

draw 1 more

draw 1 more

Note for parent: This page prepares your child for adding. Ask 'How many altogether?' 'Three spiders and one more spider makes four spiders altogether.'

Circle the correct answers.

One helicopter flies away.
How many are left?

3
2
1

One mouse runs away.
How many are left?

3
5
4

One butterfly flies away.
How many are left?

2
3
4

One car drives away.
How many are left?

1
2
3

Note for parent: This page prepares your child for subtracting or taking away. Play a game: show five fingers, hide one finger to show 'one less'. How many fingers are left?

Add one

Point to each picture and count the objects.
Say the numbers out loud.
Write the totals in the boxes.

$$1 + 1 = 2$$

$$2 + 1 = \boxed{}$$

$$3 + 1 = \boxed{}$$

Note for parent: Counting on shows that the last number counted gives the total. Hold up two fingers, then hold up one more. Two fingers add one finger makes (one, two,) three fingers altogether.

Take away one

Count the animals. Take one away.
How many are left?
Write in the missing numbers.

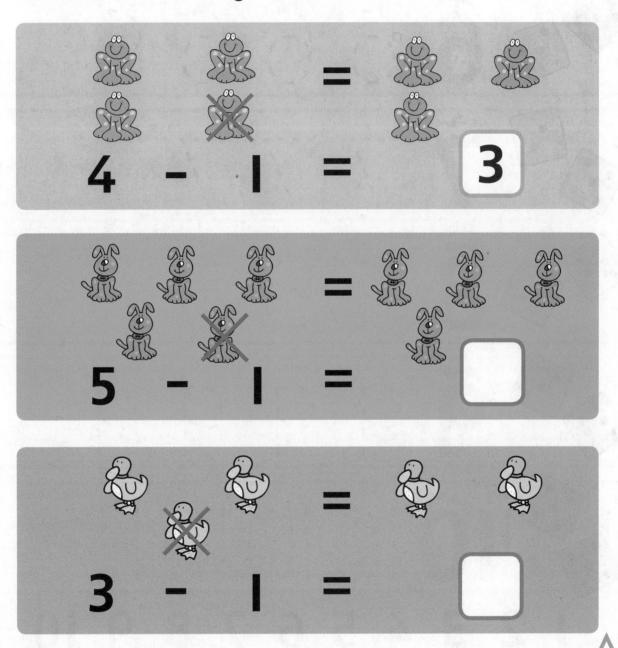

4 - 1 = 3

5 - 1 =

3 - 1 =

Note for parent: This activity helps your child understand that taking away one object leaves one less. Hold up five fingers. Fold down one. How many are still up?

Numbers up to 10

Count the spots on the dice. Point to the numbers.
Trace them with your finger. Write the numbers.

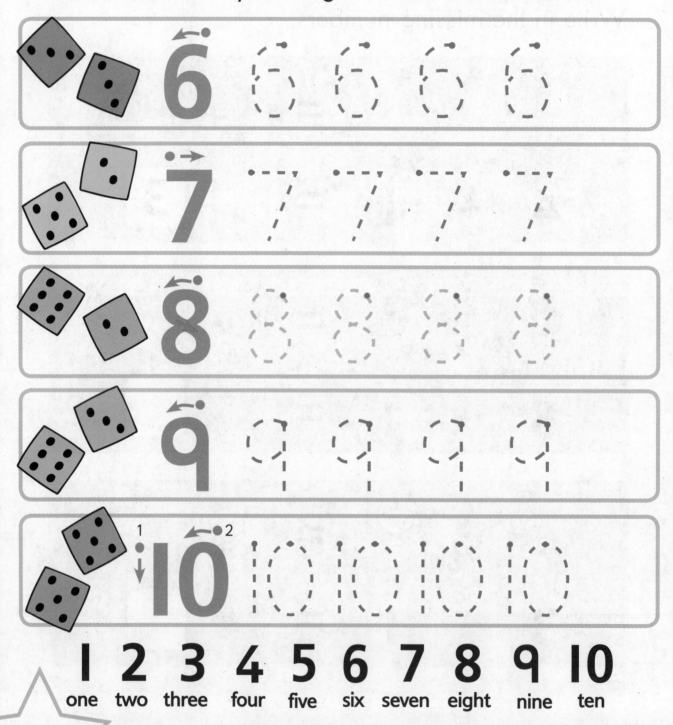

1	2	3	4	5	6	7	8	9	10
one	two	three	four	five	six	seven	eight	nine	ten

How many?

Count the number of each thing and write the answers in the boxes.

ducklings ☐
horse ☐
flowers ☐
bees ☐
trees ☐
pigs ☐
sunflowers ☐
cows ☐
wheels ☐
sheep ☐

Colour the picture.

Note for parent: This activity gives your child practice in counting up to ten. Ask your child to guess (estimate) how many of each thing first. Count to see how close they are.

13

Ordering numbers

Write in the missing numbers.

Note for parent: This activity gives your child practice in counting forwards and backwards. Play countdown games. Who will be first to finish? 5, 4, 3, 2, 1, go!

Counting in 2s

Write the totals in the boxes.
There are two spots altogether.

2

Draw two arms on each teddy.
How many arms altogether?

Draw two legs on each duck.
How many legs altogether?

Draw two ears on each cat.
How many ears altogether?

   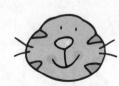

Note for parent: This activity gives your child practice in counting in twos up to ten. Put 10 counters in groups of two. Point and count to each group – 2, 4, 6, 8, 10.

15

Adding numbers

Look at the sums. They use a number track to find the answers. Write in the answers.

1 + 2 = 3

The frog starts on number 1. He makes two jumps forwards and lands on number 3.

1 2 3 4 5 6 7 8 9 10

2 + 3 = ☐

1 2 3 4 5 6 7 8 9 10

4 + 4 = ☐

1 2 3 4 5 6 7 8 9 10

5 + 4 = ☐

1 2 3 4 5 6 7 8 9 10

Note for parent: This activity shows your child how to use a number track to add. Start at a number and add on another number without beginning from 1 each time.

Taking away

Look at the sums. They use a number track to find the answers. Write in the answers.

$3 - 2 =$ **1** The frog starts on number 3. He makes two jumps backwards and lands on number 1.

| 1 | 2 | 3 | 4 | 5 | 6 | 7 | 8 | 9 | 10 |

$5 - 2 =$ ☐

| 1 | 2 | 3 | 4 | 5 | 6 | 7 | 8 | 9 | 10 |

$7 - 4 =$ ☐

| 1 | 2 | 3 | 4 | 5 | 6 | 7 | 8 | 9 | 10 |

$10 - 3 =$ ☐

| 1 | 2 | 3 | 4 | 5 | 6 | 7 | 8 | 9 | 10 |

Note for parent: This activity shows how to take away (subtract) using a number track. Explain that taking something away means you end up with less.

17

Big and small

big

small

small

big

Tick the big animal.

Draw the small animal.

Tick the small cake.

Draw the big cake.

Note for parent: This activity helps your child to compare sizes. Use words such as small, smaller, smallest, big, bigger, biggest.

Heavy and light

heavy   **light**

light   **heavy**

Tick the heavy animal.

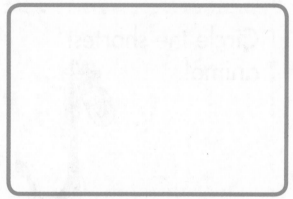

Draw the heavy animal.

Tick the light object.

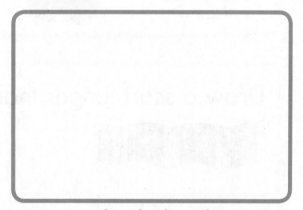

Draw the light object.

Note for parent: This activity helps your child to compare different weights. Use words such as light, lighter, lightest, heavy, heavier, heaviest.

Tall, short and long

 tall

 long

 short

Circle the shortest animal.

Circle the tallest house.

Draw a scarf longer than this one.

Note for parent: Measure the sheight of your child and other family members. Compare them using words such as tall, taller, tallest, short, shorter, shortest.

More or less?

Circle the cake with more candles.

Circle the ladybird with less spots.

Which boxes have more in them? Tick the one you think has more. Then count to see if you are right.

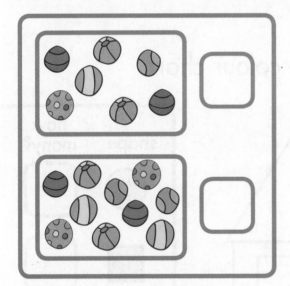
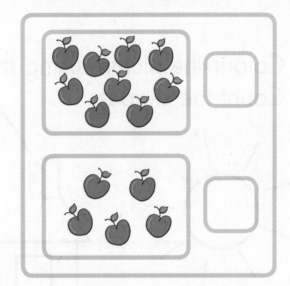

Draw a nest with more birds in it than this one.

Note for parent: This activity helps your child understand estimating and the terms 'more' and 'less'.

21

Shapes

Trace over the dotted shapes. Draw them below.
Then colour them in.

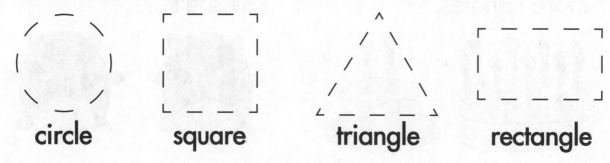

circle square triangle rectangle

Colour the picture using the colour chart.
Count the shapes.

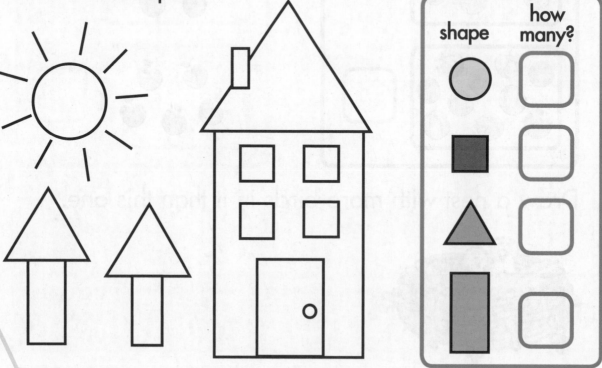

Patterns

Finish the patterns.

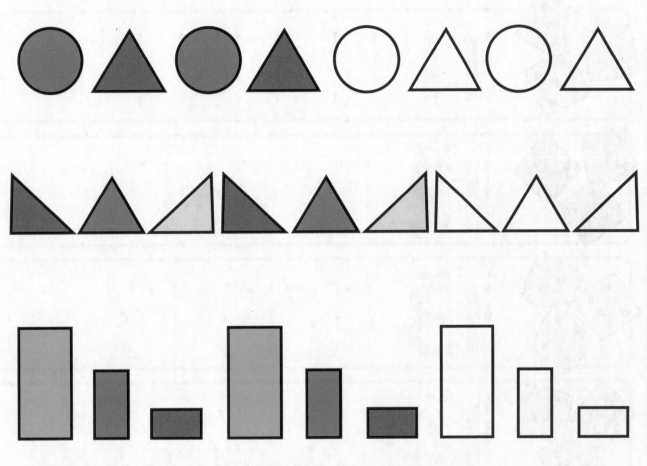

Make up your own pattern using shapes.

Note for parent: Recognising patterns in shapes helps your child with reasoning and problem solving. Make simple repeating patterns with beads or buttons.

23

Numbers up to 20

Count the spots on the dice. Point to the numbers.
Trace them with your finger. Write the numbers.

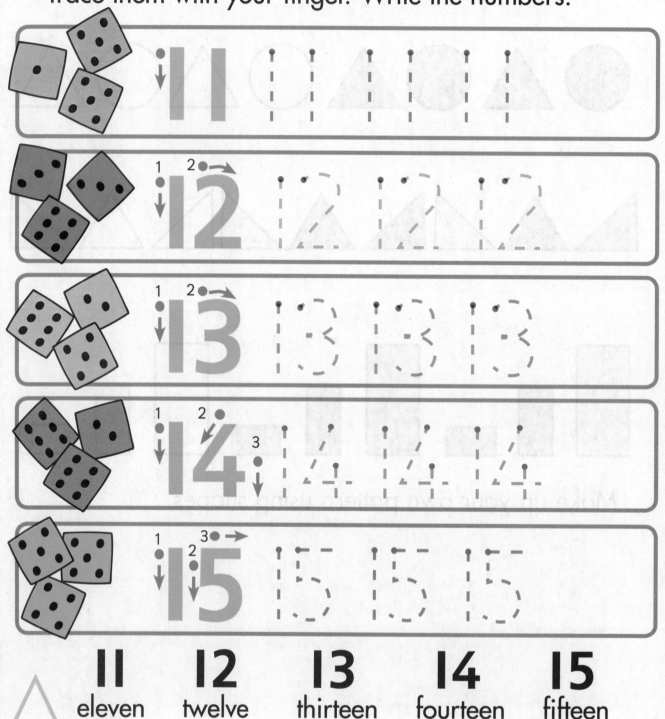

11 eleven   **12** twelve   **13** thirteen   **14** fourteen   **15** fifteen

Note for parent: These pages will give your child practice in counting up to twenty.
It is important that your child learns to write numbers correctly.

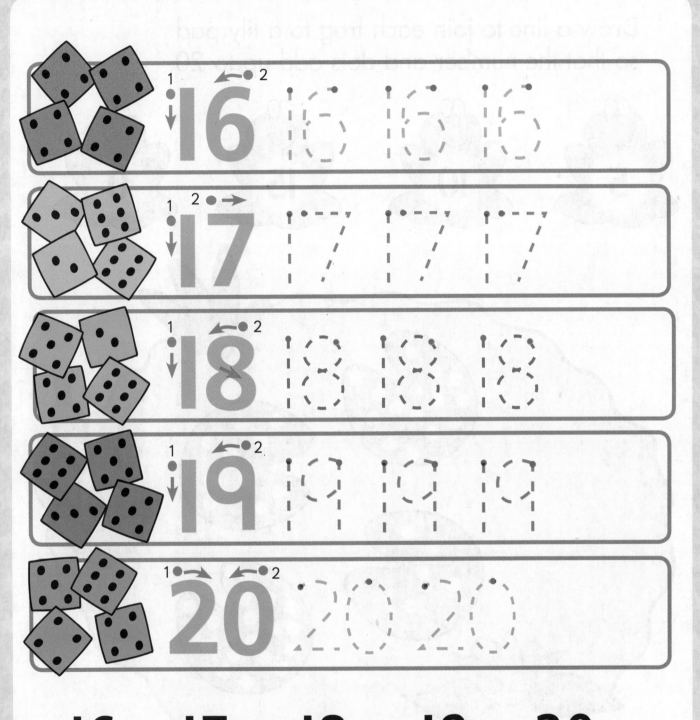

16
sixteen

17
seventeen

18
eighteen

19
nineteen

20
twenty

Hop up to 20

Draw a line to join each frog to a lily pad
so that the number and dots add up to 20.

Note for parent: This will teach your child some number bonds up to 20, in multiples of 5.
These simple addition facts makes adding and multiplying much easier.

How many?

How many marbles in each jar? Make a guess. Count to see if you are right. Draw more marbles in each jar to make 20.

guess

count

guess

count

guess

count

guess

count

Note for parent: This activity gives practice in estimating. Ask questions such as 'Do you think there are more than 10?' 'Do you think there are less than 20?'

27

Doubles

Copy the dots in the boxes to make doubles.
Count how many dots altogether. Write the answers
in the boxes.

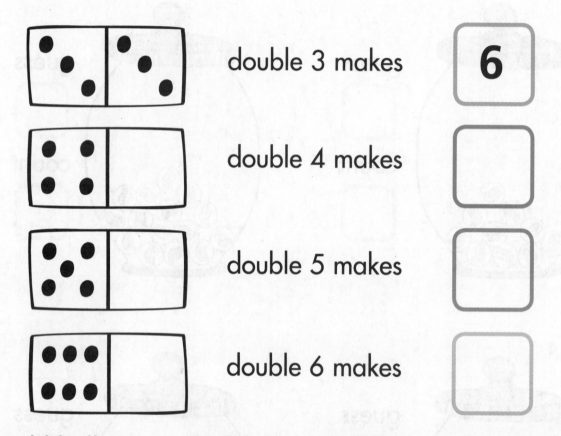

double 3 makes **6**

double 4 makes

double 5 makes

double 6 makes

Add balloons to double the number that each clown
holds.

Note for parent: This activity gives practice in understanding doubles.

Colour half of the spots on each ladybird.

Share the pizza equally between the two children.
Draw a line to cut the pizza in half.

Note for parent: This activity gives practice in understanding halves.

29

Money

How much? Add up the money in each purse.

total = [ ]

total = [ ]

total = [ ]

total = [ ]

Circle the items you would buy. They must add up to 20.

pencil

apple

banana

cake

marble

ice cream

Note for parent: This activity gives additional practice in adding up to 20. Use real coins to match the money in each purse – this will help your child to count out and add them up.

Time

Fill in the missing numbers.

What time is it?

It is [ ] o'clock.

It is [ ] o'clock

It is [ ] o'clock

It is [ ] o'clock

It is [ ] o'clock

It is [ ] o'clock

It is [ ] o'clock

Answers

Page 5

2 (butterflies), 1 (bee),
3 (ladybirds), 4 (spiders),
5 (snails)

Page 6

Page 7

Page 8

3 (cars), 2 (bees), 5 (socks)
4 (spiders)

Page 9

2 (helicopters), 4 (mice),
3 (butterflies), 1 (car)

Page 10

3 (teddies), 4 (ladybirds)

Page 11

4 (dogs), 2 (ducks)

Page 13

8 (ducklings), 1 (horse),
10 (flowers), 9 (bees), 4 (trees),
5 (pigs), 7 (sunflowers), 2 (cows),
3 (wheels), 6 (sheep)

Page 14

Page 15

4 (teddy arms), 6 (duck legs),
8 (cat ears)

Page 16

$2 + 3 = 5$, $4 + 4 = 8$
$5 + 4 = 9$

Page 17

$5 - 2 = 3$, $7 - 4 = 3$
$10 - 3 = 7$

Page 18

Page 19

Page 20

Page 21

Page 22

Page 23

Page 26

Page 27

Page 28

Double 4 makes 8
Double 5 makes 10
Double 6 makes 12

Page 29

Page 30

Page 31

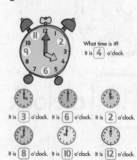